My Grief Diary

A WORKBOOK THROUGH GRIEF

A companion guide & confidante
in the aftermath of loss

Creator of award-winning Grief Diaries
Co-Founder, International Grief Institute
LYNDA CHELDELIN FELL

WITH

Founder, National Grief Awareness Day
ANGIE CARTWRIGHT

Grief Diaries
My Grief Diary – 1st ed.
A companion guide & confidante in the aftermath of loss
Lynda Cheldelin Fell/Angie Cartwright
Grief Diaries www.GriefDiaries.com

Cover Design by AlyBlue Media, LLC
Interior Design by AlyBlue Media LLC
Published by AlyBlue Media, LLC

ISBN: 978-1-944328-87-0
AlyBlue Media, LLC
Ferndale, WA 98248
www.AlyBlueMedia.com

This book is designed to provide informative narrations to readers. It is sold with the understanding that the writers, authors or publisher is not engaged to render any type of psychological, legal, or any other kind of professional advice. The content is the sole expression and opinion of the authors and writers. No warranties or guarantees are expressed or implied by the choice to include any of the content in this book. Neither the publisher nor the author or writers shall be liable for any physical, psychological, emotional, financial, or commercial damages including but not limited to special, incidental, consequential or other damages. Our views and rights are the same: You are responsible for your own choices, actions and results.

PRINTED IN THE UNITED STATES OF AMERICA

Dedication

In loving memory of
Rhonda Sue Newsome
Alyssa Victoria Yvonne Fell

CONTENTS

About This Workbook

Grief is a long, hard journey that is as unique to each griever as one's fingerprint. While there is no single cure for grief, there are numerous tools that offer comfort and encouragement along your journey. **My Grief Diary** is one of these tools.

Broken into two parts, this workbook allows you to express your grief in a safe and comforting manner, like you're among friends. And you are, for we compiled this workbook from our hearts to yours. The first part offers assignments designed to help you face your grief. The second part offers assignments to help you learn how to live again as you reassemble the pieces. Throughout you will find personal, candid reflections from both of us.

Healing is a collaborative effort between yourself, your family and friends, your healthcare providers, and even us. We encourage you to share the assignments with your doctor, counselor, and/or therapist. As healing is not a process to be rushed, neither is your completion of this workbook. In fact, we encourage you to take your time with each assignment, possibly days and even weeks. There is nothing to be gained by rushing, and everything to be gained by taking your time.

Please note that we use the word "heal." That is an important concept to keep close to your heart. Grief turns one's life upside down, shreds it to pieces. And healing takes time and, well let's face it, we have nothing but time in the aftermath of loss. Maybe your life will never be the same as it was, but with hard work, lots of patience, and tender loving care of yourself, you can find your footing once again and even feel moments of peace and joy. We are living proof of that.

Please use us as your inspiration whenever the waves of grief wash over you, let us be your umbrella during the moments of torrential downpour. We have walked and survived the storms of grief to find that peace, and even joy, do indeed exist in the aftermath. We know you can do it too, and we want to help. In fact, we'll be your biggest cheerleaders, so don't give up! We are here every step of the way.

From our hearts to your heart,

Lynda Cheldelin Fell & Angie Cartwright

Hugs are and always will be
better than words.

LYNDA CHELDELIN FELL

My Grief Diary

From the Authors

Dear friend,

Thank you for participating in My Grief Diary. I too have suffered from devastating grief, and was looking for a way out. The lessons contained in this workbook proved immensely helpful, and we want to share them with you. Don't be afraid to message me if you have any questions about these assignments, as we are here to help one another. Also, I invite you to join me in both our open and closed groups on Facebook including Grief the Unspoken, National Grief Awareness Day, and Grief Diaries. Grief is a journey that is best walked with others, and we would be honored to have you join us.

With all my love,

Angie Cartwright
Founder, National Grief Awareness Day
angie@nationalgriefawarenessday.com

Dear friend,

Helen Keller once said, "Walking with a friend in the dark is better than walking alone in the light." Moving through grief is one of the hardest challenges we'll ever face and, although each journey is as unique as one's own fingerprint, it's important to know you are not alone in the dark. This workbook is designed to find you in the black abyss of profound sorrow and be your companion along the journey. It offers the very tools we used ourselves to help navigate our own kaleidoscope of emotions, and we are honored to share it with you. May it bring you comfort, healing, and hope.

Warmest regards,

Lynda Cheldelin Fell
Creator of award-winning Grief Diaries
lynda@lyndafell.com | www.LyndaFell.com | www.GriefDiaries.com | www.IGIeducation.org

Important Message to Abuse Victims

If you have experienced sexual abuse, emotional abuse, physical abuse, alcoholism, or drug addiction, you have experienced grief that goes along with it. In your inventory list, you most likely have people who have caused you this pain. When we experience abuse of any kind, we grieve loss of security, loss of normalcy, and loss of trust. We can live in overwhelming fear, and that fear can dominate our other relationships. Naturally, it can be very difficult to write life letters to those who have abused you.

When we forgive someone, it has nothing to do with them. We will never forget nor condone their behavior. It's important that you realize when we can't forgive the person, that person is still hurting you. When we apply our grief inventory to these kinds of relationships, we can start to be free from those who kept us imprisoned. Remember forgiveness is not about condoning their behaviour....it is about freeing yourself.

If you are being abused or suffer from addiction, we suggest you seek professional help. If you need help in finding resources in your area please message us, and we will do our best to get you help. Reading your life letters to your counselor is suggested to provide you with the security you need when doing this.

PART ONE

Facing Our Grief

It's okay to cry. Giving in to the tears is terrifying, like freefalling without a parachute. But it's vital to our wellbeing as we process the deep anguish.
LYNDA CHELDELIN FELL

ASSIGNMENT 1

Listing Our Grief

DIRECTIONS:

Write down all your losses. If there are more than ten losses, keep writing. Note any memories or thoughts that come up associated with each loss. Please don't rush this. Keep your diary handy and allow yourself some time to keep writing.

LOSS 1 _____

Memory: _____

Thought: _____

_____

_____

_____

LOSS 2 _____

Memory: _____

Thought: _____

_____

_____

_____

LOSS 3 _____

Memory: _____

Thought: _____

_____

_____

_____

Notes, thoughts & doodles:

One of the first things I realized as I have been on this journey is that

I was unaware of all the grief in my heart. If you would have asked me two

years ago who I have grieved over, I could have listed my loved ones and my pets.

ANGIE CARTWRIGHT

LOSS 4 _____

Memory: _____

Thought: _____

_____

_____

_____

_____

LOSS 5 _____

Memory: _____

Thought: _____

_____

_____

_____

_____

LOSS 6 _____

Memory: _____

Thought: _____

_____

_____

_____

_____

LOSS 7 _____

Memory: _____

Thought: _____

_____

_____

_____

_____

LOSS 8 _____

Memory: _____

Thought: _____

_____

_____

_____

Notes, thoughts & doodles:

One laugh can scatter a hundred griefs.

Go ahead, try it.

LYNDA CHELDELIN FELL

LOSS 9 _____

Memory:_____

Thought:_____

_____

_____

_____

_____

LOSS 10_____

Memory:_____

Thought:_____

_____

_____

_____

_____

More thoughts:

Notes, thoughts & doodles:

A hug is where healing begins.
LYNDA CHELDELIN FELL

ASSIGNMENT 2

We Grieve Many Things

Grief is the normal process of reacting to a loss, any loss. The loss may be physical (such as a death), social (such as divorce), or occupational (such as a job). Now that you have listed your main losses in the last assignment, we want you to look again for more losses in your life. You might not associate them with grief, but grief is usually around when we have these types of losses. Here are other kinds of losses:

- Divorce
- Retirement
- Loss of a relationship
- Fragile health

- Addiction
- Abuse of any kind
- Financial loss
- Empty nest

- Moving
- Spending time in prison
- Having a loved one in prison

DIRECTIONS:

As you did in assignment #1, fully explore your memories around each loss. Write down your thoughts, feelings, and experiences associated with each one. Take your time, do not rush this assignment.

LOSS 11_____

Memory:_____

Thought:_____

_____

_____

LOSS 12_____

Memory:_____

Thought:_____

_____

_____

LOSS 13_____

Memory:_____

Thought:_____

_____

_____

Notes, thoughts & doodles:

It's common to feel that secondary losses pale in comparison to losing a loved one, but the fact remains that we grieve all losses. It's important to validate all the losses we've been through, not just the obvious ones.
LYNDA CHELDELIN FELL

LOSS 14_____

Memory:_____

Thought:_____

_____

_____

_____

_____

LOSS 15_____

Memory:_____

Thought:_____

_____

_____

_____

_____

LOSS 16_____

Memory:_____

Thought:_____

_____

_____

_____

_____

LOSS 17_____

Memory:_____

Thought:_____

_____

_____

_____

_____

LOSS 18_____

Memory:_____

Thought:_____

_____

_____

Notes, thoughts & doodles:

when we treat others with compassion,
we empower their souls.
ANGIE CARTWRIGHT

LOSS 19

Memory:

Thought:

LOSS 20

Memory:

Thought:

At first I hated the idea of journaling. But when I finally put
pen to paper, I unexpectedly found it quite healing and therapeutic.

LYNDA CHELDELIN FELL

Notes, thoughts & doodles:

Kindness is a language everyone understands.
LYNDA CHELDELIN FELL

ASSIGNMENT 3

The Bigger Picture

DIRECTIONS:

Combine all losses from assignments #1 and #2 here. We want them all compiled into one list. If you have thought of any more losses, add those too.

1. _____
2. _____
3. _____
4. _____
5. _____
6. _____
7. _____
8. _____
9. _____
10. _____
11. _____
12. _____
13. _____
14. _____
15. _____
16. _____
17. _____
18. _____
19. _____
20. _____

Notes, thoughts & doodles:

Not every day is beautiful,
but there is beauty in every day.
LYNDA CHELDELIN FELL

ASSIGNMENT 4

Reacting to Loss

DIRECTIONS:
Answer the following questions.

How do you think your losses have affected you?
Answer: _____

_____

_____

_____

Did you ever express the grief you experienced?
Answer: _____

_____

_____

_____

How did you handled it?
Answer: _____

_____

_____

_____

Have you ever been able to grieve openly about it?
Answer: _____

_____

_____

_____

Notes, thoughts & doodles:

There is a huge difference between living in
the past and remembering the past.
ANGIE CARTWRIGHT

Notes, thoughts & doodles:

DIRECTIONS:

Write a summary about your losses based upon what you have discovered by completing the last four assignments. What have you discovered so far about you and your life? Please don't rush this. Keep your diary handy and allow yourself some days to keep writing.

_____

_____

_____

_____

_____

_____

_____

_____

_____

_____

_____

_____

_____

_____

_____

_____

_____

_____

_____

_____

_____

_____

_____

ASSIGNMENT 5

Reacting to Pain

DIRECTIONS:

List all the ways you reacted to pain in the past. Find a place where you can be alone, a place where you feel safe. It may be your bed, the park, even sitting alone in your car. Shut your phone off. Take several deep breaths. Now look back on your life and **identify how you reacted to pain.**

How did you react to pain in the past? Try to go back as far as you can remember. Please don't rush this. Keep your diary handy and allow yourself some days to keep writing and note any memories or thoughts that come up associated with each pain.

_____

_____

_____

_____

_____

_____

_____

_____

_____

_____

_____

_____

_____

_____

_____

_____

_____

_____

_____

_____

_____

Notes, thoughts & doodles:

I ask myself in everything I do:
did I give kindness or did I rob someone of joy?
LYNDA CHELDELIN FELL

ASSIGNMENT 6

Fear

DIRECTIONS:

List your fears. Take a deep breath and ask yourself the following questions: What am I afraid of? What scares me? Do I stop myself from healing because I'm afraid? Take another deep breath, pause for a moment, and then list your fears. Any fear....from spiders to sex. Leave nothing out. No fear is dumb.

FEAR #1: _____

Thoughts associated with this fear:_____

_____

_____

FEAR #2: _____

Thoughts associated with this fear:_____

_____

_____

FEAR #3: _____

Thoughts associated with this fear:_____

_____

_____

FEAR #4: _____

Thoughts associated with this fear:_____

_____

_____

FEAR #5: _____

Thoughts associated with this fear:_____

_____

Notes, thoughts & doodles:

What I have discovered in myself is that I have many fears!
Everyone is different, but some of my fears include dying, trying
new things, meeting new people, being accepted, and trusting people.
ANGIE CARTWRIGHT

FEAR #7:_____

Thoughts associated with this fear:_____

_____

_____

FEAR #8:_____

Thoughts associated with this fear:_____

_____

_____

FEAR #9:_____

Thoughts associated with this fear:_____

_____

_____

FEAR #10: _____

Thoughts associated with this fear:_____

_____

_____

Now answer these questions:

Do you let fear run your life? _____

_____

_____

Do you act like you are not fearful, but secretly feel paralyzed? _____

_____

_____

_____

Are you ready to take your power back and walk through some fear? _____

_____

_____

Notes, thoughts & doodles:

I already know sorrow. Today I choose joy.
LYNDA CHELDELIN FELL

INVENTORY LIST

DIRECTIONS:

This assignment may be tough, but using your compiled list from Assignment #3, write down everything positive about each event listed, and then write down everything painful about each event listed. This may be difficult with someone who caused you nothing but pain, but try to come up with one positive thing about them. Did they provide you with food or shelter? Did they have a sense of humor? The positive list may be very small for some events, but try. Below are two examples.

Loss #1: My mother died

Positive (good)
She gave me life
She never physically hurt me
She kept trying
She loved people
She was a good listener

Painful (bad):
Her addiction
She left when I was young
Taking us to foster care

Loss #2: I have fibromyalgia (loss of health)

Positive (good):
It has helped me to be more patient
It has helped me to be more compassionate
It has helped me to slow down and not rush through life

Painful (bad):
I can't do what I used to do
It lowered my self esteem
I am not sexual or even interested

Note: If you start to feel guilty, keep going. Be honest with yourself. Please don't rush this. Keep your diary handy and allow yourself some days to keep writing and note any positive or painful experiences associated with the each loss. Be sure to include the grief you feel for those still living.

Up to this point you have done a lot of work. Congratulate yourself! I believe the hardest work in the world is looking within. By this time in my own workbook, I was able to see how I grieved over so much more than I thought. I also was able to see how I reacted to pain and how much fear there was in most areas of my life. – Angie

Notes, thoughts & doodles:

Everything looked good on the outside,

but on the inside I was dying.

ANGIE CARTWRIGHT

LOSS 1: _____

Positive: _____   Painful: _____

Positive: _____   Painful: _____

Positive: _____   Painful: _____

Positive: _____   Painful: _____

LOSS 2: _____

Positive: _____   Painful: _____

Positive: _____   Painful: _____

Positive: _____   Painful: _____

Positive: _____   Painful: _____

LOSS 3: _____

Positive: _____   Painful: _____

Positive: _____   Painful: _____

Positive: _____   Painful: _____

Positive: _____   Painful: _____

LOSS 4: _____

Positive: _____   Painful: _____

Positive: _____   Painful: _____

Positive: _____   Painful: _____

Positive: _____   Painful: _____

Notes, thoughts & doodles:

How do we survive grief?

One breath at a time.

LYNDA CHELDELIN FELL

LOSS 5: _____

Positive: _____   Painful: _____

Positive: _____   Painful: _____

Positive: _____   Painful: _____

Positive: _____   Painful: _____

LOSS 6: _____

Positive: _____   Painful: _____

Positive: _____   Painful: _____

Positive: _____   Painful: _____

Positive: _____   Painful: _____

LOSS 7: _____

Positive: _____   Painful: _____

Positive: _____   Painful: _____

Positive: _____   Painful: _____

Positive: _____   Painful: _____

LOSS 8: _____

Positive: _____   Painful: _____

Positive: _____   Painful: _____

Positive: _____   Painful: _____

Positive: _____   Painful: _____

Notes, thoughts & doodles:

Grief has nothing to do with a
person being strong or weak.
ANGIE CARTWRIGHT

LOSS 9: _____

Positive: _____   Painful: _____

Positive: _____   Painful: _____

Positive: _____   Painful: _____

Positive: _____   Painful: _____

LOSS 10: _____

Positive: _____   Painful: _____

Positive: _____   Painful: _____

Positive: _____   Painful: _____

Positive: _____   Painful: _____

More thoughts:

Notes, thoughts & doodles:

My Ten Rules of Grief
GRIEF RULE #1: There are no rules. Period.
LYNDA CHELDELIN FELL

ASSIGNMENT 8

The True Story

"Fact Finding" and "Fact Facing" is vital to our healing process, to allow ourselves to tell the true story of our loss. Grief can keep us lost in a place where we only tell ourselves the story we believe we can handle because our heart is so broken. As we can see by this point, each loss has both positive and negative aspects. When grieving, we focus *many times on the negative*. But when we do, we often feel guilty. When we remember the good times, we can often feel it is just too much to think about, so we become lost in grief.

For example, I shared addiction with my mother. In 2003, I started the healing process for myself. She joined me years later. After several years we both relapsed. It was one of the saddest times in my life. I went back to sobriety after a few months and she did not. Twenty eight days later she died from a drug overdose. Here are some of the things I told myself after losing her:

- "I am a horrible daughter. I never helped her. She was always annoying me."
- "If I would have went that night she would have been alive today."
- "My mother just abandoned me again. She just gave up."
- "If I wouldn't have relapsed, she would be here today."

Sound familiar? That's because these thoughts and feelings are normal for grieving people. But how do we find a way out? Society tells us just to not think of those things, yet it is virtually impossible. We are grieving, so it's natural that we continuously try to make sense out of something that doesn't make sense.

DIRECTION:

For each loss listed on your Inventory List, write the thoughts you tell yourself about this relationship or event, whether they are true or false. Please remember to be 100% honest. The more honest you are with yourself, the better you'll feel from these exercises. Then ask yourself this question for each loss listed: What do I feel guilty about with this relationship or loss? Note: Please don't rush this. Keep your diary handy and allow yourself some days to keep writing and note any feelings of guilt or memories associated with each loss.

LOSS #1: _____

My Thoughts: _____

_____

I feel guilty about this loss because: _____

_____

Notes, thoughts & doodles:

My Ten Rules of Grief
GRIEF RULE #2: I will grieve my way, not your way. My way may
not make sense to you, but it doesn't make sense to me either.
LYNDA CHELDELIN FELL

LOSS #2: _____

My Thoughts: _____

_____

_____

I feel guilty about this loss because: _____

_____

_____

LOSS #3: _____

My Thoughts: _____

_____

_____

I feel guilty about this loss because: _____

_____

_____

LOSS #4: _____

My Thoughts: _____

_____

_____

I feel guilty about this loss because: _____

_____

_____

Notes, thoughts & doodles:

My Ten Rules of Grief
GRIEF RULE #3: The grief timeline is long. If I begin to move on in two months,
something is wrong. If I begin to move forward in two years, be impressed.
LYNDA CHELDELIN FELL

LOSS #5: _____

My Thoughts: _____

_____

_____

I feel guilty about this loss because: _____

_____

_____

LOSS #6: _____

My Thoughts: _____

_____

_____

I feel guilty about this loss because: _____

_____

_____

LOSS #7: _____

My Thoughts: _____

_____

_____

I feel guilty about this loss because: _____

_____

_____

Notes, thoughts & doodles:

My Ten Rules of Grief
GRIEF RULE #4: Hugs are and always will be better than words.
LYNDA CHELDELIN FELL

LOSS #8: _____

My Thoughts: _____

_____

_____

I feel guilty about this loss because: _____

_____

_____

LOSS #9: _____

My Thoughts: _____

_____

_____

I feel guilty about this loss because: _____

_____

_____

LOSS #10:_____

My Thoughts: _____

_____

_____

I feel guilty about this loss because: _____

_____

_____

Notes, thoughts & doodles:

My Ten Rules of Grief
GRIEF RULE #5: When you ask me how I am, I
will always answer politely. The truth is too ugly.
LYNDA CHELDELIN FELL

Accepting Ourselves

As we can see from the last assignment, we tell ourselves things that may not be true. Even if they are true, it is necessary to forgive ourselves. We are all human, and there is no one on earth that is perfect.

Go back to the inventory list in assignment #7. Are you now willing to list truthful facts about your relationships and losses? Did you love the person? Did you try to be kind? Did you cause their illness? Please note that these are general questions.

With relationships that were nothing but bad (such as physical/sexual abuse), this may be difficult or even impossible to do. You can choose to just move forward at this point or you can privately look to see how you have grown as a stronger, more compassionate, more aware or smarter person because of the event.

Note: If you need to pause and take a deep breath and get a glass of water, this would be a good time to do so. Please don't rush this. Keep your diary handy and allow yourself some days to keep writing and note any truths about the person or loss that come up. There is no right way or wrong way to do this assignment.

When I started doing my grief work, the story that I would tell myself and the inner dialogue started to change for the good! As you learned from my story about my mother in a previous assignment, here are the facts I know today:

- My mother loved me and told me that every time she saw me. She showed me love with her actions.

- My mother was a grown woman and was able to make her own choices. A few nights before she passed we had a conversation and I told her she needed medical attention. She chose not to go.

- My mother tried to make changes in her life throughout her life.

- My mother had a disease, she was in pain and wanted to treat her pain. The night she overdosed she was treating her pain. She was powerless over her addiction.

- I have helped my mother many times over in her life. I took her into my home many times. I went and picked her up and brought her to town to receive help many times. If she needed something I was always there for her.

-Angie

Notes, thoughts & doodles:

My Ten Rules of Grief
GRIEF RULE #6: If I question my faith, do not condemn me. It is normal.
LYNDA CHELDELIN FELL

ASSIGNMENT 10

Life Letters of Empowerment

Now it is time to take all the information you have gathered for each loss and put them into Life Letters. These letters can be read by the graveside or at a place that brings you peace. Some find it comforting to imagine the person sitting with you on the couch or across the kitchen table. If it is not possible or you don't like that idea, choose a place that brings you some peace. You also can read your letter to your minister, counselor or caring friend, if you desire.

Please note that your letter may be to someone who is still alive, and we find we're grieving the broken relationship. Maybe you and your siblings are not getting along. It may be over the loss of your parent, or you may not get along with them because of alcoholism. For whatever reason, you have lost that relationship and it can cause our hearts to be broken. We grieve for the relationship to be healed. It may seem weird to write a life letter to someone who is living, but these letters will not be read to them personally. But they are as vital as any other letter.

Here are more ways we grieve the living:
- We have a loved one in prison
- We are adopted and don't know our birth parents
- Our loved one has left for active duty in the services
- We are divorcing

These experiences are just as important as all the others. In time, you may wish to share your letter with them but do not rush this process. It is perfectly ok to imagine them sitting with you and read them the letter or read it to minister, counselor or caring friend.

DIRECTIONS:
Create a Life Letter for each inventory item. Each letter will contain the following parts:
- Forgiveness
- Amends (if needed)
- Thank you
- Closing statement, such as "See you soon," or "Good bye," or "I send you peace."

Letters about other losses such as health, empty nest, moving, etc. are just as vital as the letters to our loved ones. Note: Take your time with each letter. If things change over time from when you write these letters, write one or more new ones anytime you feel the need.

EXAMPLE LETTER #1

Dear Fibro,

I need to write to you to express my feelings. I have a few things I want to say. First of all, I <u>forgive</u> you for taking over my life. I forgive you for the pain you caused in me and my family. I also want to <u>thank you</u>. Since you have arrived in my body, I have learned a lot about myself and how strong I am. You have taught me patience with myself and others. I thank you for teaching me to not judge someone who may not feel good. I have more compassion and understanding than ever before. I am taking my life back. There is more to Angie I have learned, and I thank you for that. I have to go now. <u>Good bye.</u>

Praying for a cure,
Angie

EXAMPLE LETTER #2

Dear Mom,

I needed to write to you to express my feelings about our relationship. When you died there was so much I wanted and needed to tell you. First of all, I wanted to make <u>amends</u> for being so selfish with my time. I know you needed me and I just blew you off. I also am <u>sorry</u> for judging you and your drinking. You really tried hard and I'm so proud of you for that. I'm sorry for being so dominate in our relationship and not allowing you to mother me as you wished.

I <u>forgive</u> you for not being there for me when I was little. I forgive you for the foster homes. I forgive you for not being there for me as a child, I am a parent and have made many mistakes myself.

I wanted to <u>thank you</u> for being patient with me. I thank you for being so kind to your grandchildren and children. Thank you for passing on your beautiful sense of humor and your love for a warm blanket and a cold Pepsi. Thank you for never giving up, you always showed me that we never give up. We may fall but we have to brush ourselves off and keep going. I sure love you and miss you so much. Your legacy will live on through us.

<u>Sending you all the peace</u> in the world, Momma see ya soon!

Love your daughter,
Angie

LIFE LETTER TO LOSS #1

Dear _____,

I am writing you to express my feelings regarding _____

_____

_____

I forgive you for _____

_____

_____

_____

I want to thank you for _____

_____

_____

_____

In closing, _____

_____

_____

_____

Sincerely – Love – Warm Regards, _____

Your name

_____

LIFE LETTER TO LOSS #1

Notes, thoughts & doodles:

My Ten Rules of Grief
GRIEF RULE #7: Yes, I am blessed to have other children.
But the pain from losing one is worse than agony.
LYNDA CHELDELIN FELL

LIFE LETTER TO LOSS #2

Dear _____,

I am writing you to express my feelings regarding _____

_____

_____

I forgive you for _____

_____

_____

_____

I want to thank you for _____

_____

_____

_____

In closing, _____

_____

_____

_____

Sincerely – Love – Warm Regards,
_____

Your name
_____

Notes, thoughts & doodles:

My Ten Rules of Grief
GRIEF RULE #8: Consider me a patient of Grief United General. The first part of
my healing begins with a lengthy stay in the ICU. Please treat me accordingly.
LYNDA CHELDELIN FELL

LIFE LETTER TO LOSS #3

Dear _____,

I am writing you to express my feelings regarding _____

_____

_____

I forgive you for _____

_____

_____

_____

I want to thank you for _____

_____

_____

_____

In closing, _____

_____

_____

_____

Sincerely – Love – Warm Regards,
_____

Your name
_____

Notes, thoughts & doodles:

My Ten Rules of Grief
GRIEF RULE #9: Do not try to understand my overwhelming
emotions. Your effort will exhaust us both.
LYNDA CHELDELIN FELL

LIFE LETTER TO LOSS #4

Dear _____,

I am writing you to express my feelings regarding _____

_____

_____

I forgive you for _____

_____

_____

_____

I want to thank you for _____

_____

_____

_____

In closing, _____

_____

_____

_____

Sincerely — Love — Warm Regards, _____

Your name
_____

Notes, thoughts & doodles:

My Ten Rules of Grief
GRIEF RULE #10: Honor my pain by walking with me. Not directing me.
LYNDA CHELDELIN FELL

LIFE LETTER TO LOSS #5

Dear _____,

I am writing you to express my feelings regarding _____

_____

_____

I forgive you for _____

_____

_____

_____

I want to thank you for _____

_____

_____

_____

In closing, _____

_____

_____

_____

Sincerely – Love – Warm Regards, _____

Your name _____

Notes, thoughts & doodles:

My Ten Rules of Grief
GRIEF RULE #11: I am not a victim, I am grieving. Treat my
journey with respect and compassion, for your turn will come.
LYNDA CHELDELIN FELL

LIFE LETTER TO LOSS #6

Dear _____,

I am writing you to express my feelings regarding _____

_____

_____

I forgive you for _____

_____

_____

_____

I want to thank you for _____

_____

_____

_____

In closing, _____

_____

_____

_____

Sincerely – Love – Warm Regards,
_____

Your name
_____

LIFE LETTER TO LOSS #6

Notes, thoughts & doodles:

My Ten Rules of Grief
GRIEF RULE #12: I know this is more than the ten rules
of grief. That's because grief doesn't ever make sense.
LYNDA CHELDELIN FELL

LIFE LETTER TO LOSS #7

Dear _____,

I am writing you to express my feelings regarding _____

_____

_____

I forgive you for _____

_____

_____

_____

I want to thank you for _____

_____

_____

_____

In closing, _____

_____

_____

_____

Sincerely – Love – Warm Regards,
_____

Your name
_____

Notes, thoughts & doodles:

There's a bright future for you at every turn,
even if you miss one.

LIFE LETTER TO LOSS #8

Dear _____,

I am writing you to express my feelings regarding _____

_____

_____

I forgive you for _____

_____

_____

_____

I want to thank you for _____

_____

_____

_____

In closing, _____

_____

_____

_____

Sincerely – Love – Warm Regards,
_____

Your name
_____

Notes, thoughts & doodles:

compassion can change the world.
ANGIE CARTWRIGHT

LIFE LETTER TO LOSS #9

Dear _____,

I am writing you to express my feelings regarding _____

_____

_____

I forgive you for _____

_____

_____

I want to thank you for _____

_____

_____

_____

In closing, _____

_____

_____

_____

Sincerely – Love – Warm Regards,
_____

Your name
_____

Notes, thoughts & doodles:

The bereaved need more than just the space to grieve the loss.
They also need the space to grieve the transition.
LYNDA CHELDELIN FELL

LIFE LETTER TO LOSS #10

Dear _____,
I am writing you to express my feelings regarding _____

_____

_____

I forgive you for _____

_____

_____

_____

I want to thank you for _____

_____

_____

_____

In closing, _____

_____

_____

_____

Sincerely – Love – Warm Regards,
_____

Your name
_____

Notes, thoughts & doodles:

when grief is deepest, words are fewest.
ANN VOSKAMP

Congratulations on making it this far!

At this time, you hopefully have discovered some truths about your losses and your grief. By making it this far in the workbook, we hope you begin to experience a shift in the way you see your past, the present, and your future. It may be immediate, or it may develop slowly over a period of time. But now that you have been given some tools, when you find grief tied to any relationship, living or deceased, you can apply these steps to work through it and not become imprisoned by it.

Notes, thoughts & doodles:

There is no pain so great as the memory of joy in present grief.
AESCHYLUS

PART TWO

Facing Our Future

One night after losing my daughter Aly, I had a dream. It was one of those vivid nightmares where I was running in a frantic attempt to catch the setting sun. From behind was the pitch-black abyss of nightfall coming for me. Terrified of the darkness, I ran as fast as my legs could go toward the sun but it sank below the horizon. I had no choice but to turn around and face the darkness head on. For it was clear that if I wanted to see the sun ever again, I had to stop running west toward a sunset I couldn't catch and instead walk east through the great nightfall of grief. For just as there would be no rainbow without the rain, the sun always rises on the other side of night.

The message was clear: it was futile to avoid my grief. I had to allow it to swallow me whole. Then—and only then—would I find my way through it and out the other side.

I remember reading in a bereavement book that if we don't allow ourselves to experience the full scope of the journey, it will come back to bite us. I couldn't fathom how it could get any worse, but I knew I didn't want to test the theory. So I gave in and allowed the grief to swallow me whole. I wailed on my daughter's bedroom floor. I penned my deep emotions regardless of who might read it. I created a national radio show to openly and candidly discuss our journeys with anyone who wanted to call in. And I allowed myself to sink to the bottom of the fiery pits of hell. In turn, this lit a fire under me to find a way out.

Today I'm often asked how I manage my grief so well. Some assume that because I have found peace and joy, I'm simply avoiding my grief. Others believe that because I work in the bereavement field, I'm wallowing in self-pity. Well, which is it?

Neither. I miss my child with every breath I take. Just like you, I will always have my moments and triggers: the painful holidays, birthdays, death anniversaries, a song or smell that evokes an unexpected memory. But I have also found purpose, beauty and joy again. It takes hard work and determination to overcome profound grief, and it also takes the ability to let go and succumb to the journey. Do not be afraid of the tears, sorrow, and heartbreak; they are a natural reaction and imperative to our healing.

As you walk your own path, avail yourself of whatever bereavement tools ease your discomfort, for each one was created by someone who walked in your shoes and understands the heartache. While there are many wonderful resources available, what brings comfort to one person might irritate the next. Bereavement tools are not one-size-fits-all, so if one tool doesn't work, find another.

Lastly, grief is not something we get over, like a mountain. Rather, it is something we get through, like the rapids of Niagara Falls. Without the kayak and paddle. And plenty of falls. But it's also survivable. And if others have survived this wretched journey, why not me? And why not you?

On the following pages are the baby steps I took to put hell in my rearview mirror. At first they took great effort and lots of patience. But like any dedicated routine, it got easier over time, and the reward of finding balance in my life was worth every step.

If we can survive, so can you.

Warm regards and big hugs,

Lynda Cheldelin Fell

ASSIGNMENT 11

Self Compassion

In the long days of profound grief, exhaustion sets in easily. Everyday tasks that used to be simple now quickly become overwhelming, which adds to our tears. In addition, our memory inexplicably has deserted us entirely. Even if we muster the energy to tackle an easy household chore, we may forget what we were doing before we even begin. Sound familiar? Whether your answer is yes or no, this is a really important assignment either way....simple, but important. When I first did this assignment, I struggled. I couldn't fathom any compassionate thoughts about myself, my world had become so very dark and all my thoughts were negative. Once I began to cut myself some slack and give myself grace, I felt better. I learned a valuable lesson: I needed to love myself in order to find my way through the belly of hell.

DIRECTIONS:

Take 5 minutes to think nothing but compassionate thoughts about yourself. Find yourself a quiet spot. It can be your favorite chair, in your car, in your office, or even in your garden. Find a quiet spot, clear your head, and then think nothing but compassionate thoughts about yourself for five minutes. Not your spouse, not your children, not your coworkers, but yourself. Do this every day.

If you're struggling, here are some compassionate thoughts that may apply to you:

I have a _____
Example: good heart, gentle soul, witty personality

I make a _____
Example: good lasagna, potato salad, scrapbook, quilt

I'm a good_____
Example: friend, gardener, knitter, painter, poem writer, piano player, volunteer

People would say I'm _____
Example: funny, kind, smart, gentle, generous, patient, humble, good with my hands, creative

People would say I have a _____
Example: good sense of direction, calming voice, good handle on money, cute nose, nice smile

Once you fill in the blanks above, think about each one for a minute or two. Give yourself permission to really validate those positive qualities. Don't be afraid to add things each time you do this assignment.

Notes, thoughts & doodles:

One hug can change someone's world.
LYNDA CHELDELIN FELL

ASSIGNMENT 12

Tender Loving Care

While grieving, it is important to consider yourself in the intensive care unit of Grief United Hospital, and treat accordingly. How would the nurses treat you if you were in ICU? They would be compassionate, gentle, and allow for plenty of rest. That is exactly how you should treat yourself.

In addition, soothing sensitive parts of your body with tenderness is an attentive way to honor your emotional pain and, surprisingly, can go a long way toward comforting the whole self. If wearing fuzzy blue socks offers a smidgen of comfort, then wear them unabashedly. If whipped cream on your cocoa offers a morsel of pleasure, then indulge unapologetically. This isn't an excuse for irresponsible or unhealthy behavior. Rather, it's an opportunity to treat our five senses to something soothing….anything that offers a perception of delight. With practice, that awareness of delight will no longer require effort. And, over time, it will help to balance the sadness.

TLC suggestions:
- Shower or bathe with a lovely scented soap
- Soak in a warm tub with Epsom salts and/or a splash of bath oil
- Wear a pair of favorite socks
- Light a fragrant candle and/or listen to relaxing music
- Apply a rich lotion to your skin before bed
- Indulge in a few bites of your favorite treat
- Enjoy a mug of your favorite soothing herbal tea

<u>DIRECTIONS:</u>
List five ways you can offer yourself tender loving care, and then do <u>at least three</u> every day.

TLC #1: _____

TLC #2: _____

TLC #3: _____

TLC #4: _____

TLC #5: _____

Notes, thoughts & doodles:

She who heals others heals herself.
LYNDA CHELDELIN FELL

ASSIGNMENT 13

See the Beauty

Listening to the birds outside my bedroom window every morning was something I had loved since childhood. But when Aly died, I found myself deaf and blind to the beauty around me. My world had become colorless and silent. One morning as I struggled to get out of bed, I halfheartedly noticed the birds chirping outside my bedroom window. My heart sank as I realized that they had been chirping all along, but I was now deaf to their morning melody. Panic set in as I concluded that I would never enjoy life's beauty ever again. Briefly entertaining thoughts of suicide to escape the profound pain, I quickly ruled it out. My family had been through so much already; I couldn't dump further pain on them. But in order to survive the heartbreak, I had to find a way to allow beauty back into my life.

So on that particular morning as I lay in bed, I forced myself to listen and really *hear* the birds. Every morning from that point forward, I repeated that same exercise. With persistent practice, it became easier and then eventually effortless to appreciate the birds' chirping and singsongs. Glorious beauty and sounds have once again returned to my world.

Profound grief can appear to rob our world of all beauty. Yet the truth is, despite our suffering, beauty continues to surround us. The birds continue to sing, flowers continue to bloom, the surf continues to ebb and flow. Reconnecting to our surroundings helps us to reintegrate back into our environment.

Begin by acknowledging one small pleasantry each day. Perhaps your ears register the sound of singing birds. Or you catch the faint scent of cookies baking in a neighbor's kitchen. Or notice the sun's illumination of a nearby red rosebush. Give yourself permission to notice one pleasantry, and allow it to really register within your body and soul. Here are some suggestions:

- Hear the birds sing
- Observe some pretty cloud formations
- Visit a nearby park and listen to the children laughing
- Notice the pretty colors of blooming flowers
- Sit on a beach or at the edge of a lake
- Search for interesting rocks
- Attend a local concert, play, or comedy act
- Hike a popular trail

DIRECTIONS:

List five ways you can observe the beauty around you, and then try to accomplish <u>at least three</u> every day.

BEAUTY #1: _____

BEAUTY #2: _____

BEAUTY #3: _____

BEAUTY #4: _____

BEAUTY #5: _____

There is no medicine like hope.

ORISON SWETT MARDEN

ASSIGNMENT 14

Protect your Health

After our daughter's accident I soon found myself fighting an assortment of viruses including head colds, stomach flus, sore throats and more, compounding my already frazzled emotions. It was then when I realized how far reaching the effects of grief has, that it truly touches every part of our life including our physical health. Studies show that profound grief throws our body into "flight or fight" syndrome for months and months. This prolonged physiological response can often cause physical unbalance resulting in compromised immunity and illnesses. Thus it becomes critical to guard our physical health. Resist the urge to seek refuge in damaging substances such as alcohol or illicit drugs. Instead, nourish your body by way of healthful eating, small amounts of light exercise such as walking the dog or with a friend, and doing your best to practice good sleep hygiene. A stronger physical health can help anchor us in times of emotional upheaval. Opportunities to help protect our health:

- Practice good sleep hygiene
- Drink plenty of water
- Take a short walk, or other form of exercise, outside every day
- Limit simple carbohydrates
- Keep a light calendar and guard your time carefully, don't allow others to dictate and overflow your schedule
- If your diet isn't balanced, incorporate one healthful addition daily, such as a protein shake, fiber bar, or handful of dried blueberries

DIRECTIONS:
List five ways you can improve your health. And then ensure you incorporate at least three into your day, every day.

STEP #1: _____

STEP #2: _____

STEP #3: _____

STEP #4: _____

STEP #5: _____

Notes, thoughts & doodles:

There are two ways of spreading light:
to be the candle or the mirror that reflects it.
EDITH WHARTON

ASSIGNMENT 15

Find an Outlet

Three months after our daughter's accident, my dear husband and I sought refuge in a quaint little town on a nearby island. While browsing through the boutiques with a heavy heart, I stopped to admire a basket of highly fragrant soaps. On a whim, I decided to teach myself how to make soap and soon discovered that the soothing action of stirring a pot of fragrant ingredients proved to be very therapeutic. Thus, making Tear Soap became my outlet for many months.

For a long time in the grief journey, everything is painful. In the early days, just getting out of bed and taking a shower can be exhausting. Housecleaning, grocery shopping, and routine appointments often take a back seat or disappear altogether. As painful as it is, it's very important to find an outlet that gets you out of bed each day. Finding something to distract you from the pain, occupy your mind, and soothe your senses can be tricky, but possible. Performing a repetitive act can soothe your physical senses and calm your mood, and even result in a new craft or gifts. Although a new outlet may feel exhausting at first, this step is critical to your future well-being. It doesn't mean you have to do it forever, just focus on it for the time being. -Lynda
Possible activities include:

- Learn to mold chocolate or soap
- Take up beading
- Learn how to knit, crochet, or quilt
- Make something from your loved one's clothing
- Learn a new sport such as golf or kayaking

- Create a memorial garden
- Join Pinterest or a book club
- Renovate one room
- Volunteer at a local shelter
- Sign up for an enrichment class

DIRECTIONS:
List five possible outlets. And then take steps to start at least one.

OUTLET #1: _____

OUTLET #2: _____

OUTLET #3: _____

OUTLET #4: _____

OUTLET #5: _____

Notes, thoughts & doodles:

Grief is hell on earth. It truly is. But when walking through hell, your only option
is to keep going. Eventually the hell ends, the dark night fades to dawn, and the
sun begins to rise once again. Just keep going and you, too, will find the sunrise.
LYNDA CHELDELIN FELL

ASSIGNMENT 16

The Future

DIRECTIONS: List five small goals you would like to achieve in the next year.

GOAL #1:_____

GOAL #2:_____

GOAL #3:_____

GOAL #4:_____

GOAL #5:_____

Look hard at your goals. Is anything standing in your way of achieving them? If so, list the obstacles here.

Obstacle #1: _____

Obstacle #2: _____

Obstacle #3: _____

Obstacle #4: _____

Obstacle #5: _____

Obstacle #6: _____

Obstacle #7: _____

Obstacle #8: _____

Obstacle #9: _____

Obstacle #10: _____

For any goal with an obstacle, re-word or revise that goal here.

GOAL #1:_____

GOAL #2:_____

GOAL #3:_____

GOAL #4:_____

GOAL #5:_____

Notes, thoughts & doodles:

Once you choose hope,
anything is possible.
CHRISTOPHER REEVE

Now, list the steps needed to accomplish each goal.

EXAMPLE:

Goal: Write a book about my loss

    Step 1: Decide what I want to tell people, and why. Can I help others?

    Step 2: Decide on a title

    Step 3: Research options for getting my book published

    Step 4: Start writing 30 minutes every day

GOAL #1: _____

    Step 1: _____

    Step 2: _____

    Step 3: _____

GOAL #2: _____

    Step 1: _____

    Step 2: _____

    Step 3: _____

GOAL #3: _____

    Step 1: _____

    Step 2: _____

    Step 3: _____

GOAL #4: _____

    Step 1: _____

    Step 2: _____

    Step 3: _____

GOAL #5: _____

    Step 1: _____

    Step 2: _____

    Step 3: _____

Notes, thoughts & doodles:

I carry your kindness wherever I go.

That way your love touches far more than just me.

LYNDA CHELDELIN FELL

Dear friend,

The baby steps offered in Part 2 of this workbook are just that....baby steps. While they don't erase or invalidate the pain, the truth is that if you treat yourself kindly, allow yourself small measures of comfort, and find a healthy outlet for your grief, you'll feel better. And if you feel better, you'll cope better. These steps can not only help bring comfort, but they can also offer focus and purpose, a light in the darkness, until you find the sunshine once again.

This brings us to the end of the workbook, and a new beginning for the life ahead. It may not be the same life you had, but it is a life worth living and with time and patience, your grief dance will eventually turn into solid footing, which will lead to purposeful steps toward finding moments of peace and joy.

But remember, no matter where you are on your journey, we are always right beside you.

With all our love,

Lynda Cheldelin Fell
& Angie Cartwright

Notes, thoughts & doodles:

The beautiful thing about hope
is that it has no expiration date.
LYNDA CHELDELIN FELL

Resources

WEBSITES
Lynda Cheldelin Fell   www.lyndafell.com
Grief Diaries   www.griefdiaries.com
National Grief Awareness Day   www.nationalgriefawarenessday.com
International Grief Institute   www.internationalgriefinstitute.com

FACEBOOK PAGES
Grief the Unspoken   www.facebook.com/grieftheunspoken
Grief Diaries   www.facebook.com/GriefDiaries
National Grief Awareness Day   www.facebook.com/nationalgriefawarenessday
Angie Cartwright, Public Figure   www.facebook.com/AngieCartwrightGrief
Lynda Cheldelin Fell, Public Figure   www.facebook.com/PowerofOneHope

FACEBOOK GROUPS
CLOSED GROUPS (must ask permission to join; your posts are not visible to others outside the group)

Grief the Unspoken (GTU)   www.facebook.com/groups/griefunspoken
GTU - Grief Diaries   www.facebook.com/groups/475881435879735
GTU – Grieving Parents   www.facebook.com/groups/390815157638000
GTU – For Widows & Widowers   www.facebook.com/groups/237646546348711
GTU - Teens & Young Adults   www.facebook.com/groups/1426561724289547
GTU – Losing a Loved One to Overdose   www.facebook.com/groups/747482248681795
GTU – Candle Lighting Sanctuary   www.facebook.com/groups/1740885262803429
GTU – Prayer Room   www.facebook.com/groups/1427845387490663
GTU – Loss of a Grandparent   www.facebook.com/groups/136117183192229
GTU – Loss of a Sibling   www.facebook.com/groups/247647045348572
GTU – Loss of a Parent   www.facebook.com/groups/291760674249800
GTU – Pictures of Our Loved Ones   www.facebook.com/groups/465635070121695
GTU – Loss of fiancé, boyfriend/girlfriend   www.facebook.com/groups/158013434372416
GTU – Loss by suicide   www.facebook.com/groups/193304607475819
GTU – Venting, Screaming & Cursing Grief   www.facebook.com/groups/334595596639207

BLOGS
Confessions of a Grieving Mother   www.astrokeoflove.blogspot.com
Grief Diaries Uncensored   www.griefdiariesuncensored.blogspot.com

Notes, thoughts & doodles:

In helping others, we help ourselves.
LYNDA CHELDELIN FELL

BY LYNDA CHELDELIN FELL

My Story

When I was a kid, I wanted to be a brain surgeon. But life has a way of throwing us curve balls that force us down a different path. Sometimes those paths are most welcome, like mothering four wonderful children. My least favorite path? Losing a child. That path is a long and torturous one, and took me straight through the belly of hell.

My story began one night in 2007 when I had a vivid dream. My daughter Aly and I were passengers in a car that missed a curve in the road and sailed into a lake. The driver and I escaped the sinking car, but Aly did not. My beloved daughter was gone. The only evidence left behind was a book floating in the water where she disappeared.

Two years later, on August 5, 2009, that horrible nightmare became my reality when Aly died in a car accident. Returning home from a swim meet, the car carrying Aly was T-boned by a father coming home from work. My beautiful fifteen-year-old daughter took the brunt of the impact and died instantly. She was the only fatality.

Life couldn't get any worse, right? Wrong. Hell wasn't done with me yet. My dear sweet hubby buried his grief in the sand. He escaped into 80-hour work weeks, more wine, more food, and less talking. His blood pressure shot up, his cholesterol went off the chart, and the perfect storm arrived on June 4, 2012. My husband suddenly began drooling and couldn't speak. At age 46, my soulmate was having a major stroke.

My dear hubby lived but couldn't speak, read, or write, and his right side was paralyzed. He needed assistance just to sit up in bed. He needed full-time care. Still reeling from the loss of our daughter, I found myself again thrust into a fog of grief so thick, I couldn't see through the storm. Adrenaline and autopilot resumed their familiar place at the helm.

But I needed reassurance that the sun was on the other side of hell. As I fought my way through the storm, I discovered that helping others was a powerful way to heal my own heart. I began reaching out to individuals who were adrift and in need of a life raft. And a warm hug.

In 2013, I formed AlyBlue Media to house my mission. Comforting people who spoke my language and listening to their stories, my mission took on a life of its own and came in many forms: a radio show, film, webinars, and writing. I also hosted a national convention to bring the brokenhearted together. I had many wonderful speakers but the one who excited me most was a woman who had faced seven losses in a few short years: Martin Luther King's youngest daughter. I didn't bring Dr. Bernice King to the convention to tell us about her famous father—we already knew that story. I wanted to know how she survived.

Over the course of that weekend, I was deeply moved by complete strangers swapping stories about hardship. Touched to the core, I set out to capture them into a book series aptly named Grief Diaries. Over a hundred people in six countries shared stories in the first 8 titles published in December 2015. Now home to more than 650 writers spanning the globe, Grief Diaries has 25 titles in print with more on the way, and I've just launched our second series called Real Life Diaries.

Where am I today? Once a bereaved mother, always a bereaved mother. My heart is a bit like a broken teacup that has been glued back together. All the pieces are there but they might not fit as seamlessly as they once did. Some days the glue is strong and unyielding. Other days that glue is wet, and threatens to spring a leak. Nonetheless, that teacup still holds water. Well, mostly coffee. Strong coffee.

Life can throw a really mean curveball that blindsides even the strongest. It's important to hold out hope that the sun can be found at the end of the path. But until you find it, it's comforting to know you aren't alone. And that is what my mission all about.

For the record, I have found the sun. Some days I marvel at its beauty. Other days it hides behind clouds. But I now know those days don't last forever. And my umbrella is much stronger than it used to be.

Helen Keller once said, "Walking with a friend in the dark is better than walking alone in the light." If you too are looking for the sun, visit our village for a hug and stay for the friendship. That's why we're here—to offer you a seat in our life raft until the storm passes, and the sun begins to shine once again. I'll even let you borrow my umbrella.

Lynda Cheldelin Fell

ABOUT

LYNDA CHELDELIN FELL

Considered a pioneer in the field of inspirational hope in the aftermath of hardship and loss, Lynda Cheldelin Fell has a passion for producing groundbreaking projects that create a legacy of help, healing, and hope.

She is the creator of the award-winning Grief Diaries and Real Life Diaries book series, co-founder of International Grief Institute, and CEO of AlyBlue Media. Her repertoire of interviews include Dr. Martin Luther King's daughter, Trayvon Martin's mother, sisters of the late Nicole Brown Simpson, Pastor Todd Burpo of Heaven Is For Real and other societal newsmakers on finding healing and hope in the aftermath of life's harshest challenges. She earned four national literary awards in 2016, and is a current nominee for five national advocacy awards.

Lynda's own story began in 2007, when she had an alarming dream about her young teenage daughter, Aly. In the dream, Aly was a backseat passenger in a car that veered off the road and sailed into a lake. Aly sank with the car, leaving behind an open book floating face down on the water. Two years later, Lynda's dream became reality when her daughter was killed as a backseat passenger in a car accident while coming home from a swim meet. Overcome with grief, Lynda's forty-six-year-old husband suffered a major stroke that left him with severe disabilities, changing the family dynamics once again.

The following year, Lynda was invited to share her remarkable story about finding hope after loss, and she accepted. That cathartic experience inspired her to create groundbreaking projects spanning national events, radio, film and books to help others who share the same journey feel less alone. Now considered one of the foremost grief educators and healing facilitators in the United States, Lynda is dedicated to helping ordinary people share their own stories of survival and hope in the aftermath of loss.

lynda@lyndafell.com | www.lyndafell.com | www.griefdiaries.com | www.internationalgriefinstitute.com

BY ANGIE CARTWRIGHT

My Story

Angie Cartwright was conceived during an alcohol-fueled blackout, and born into a life of grief. Her mother was an addict and alcoholic. Angie never knew her real father.

At age three, Angie and her two-year-old sister were in a car wreck. At the wheel was her mother's current boyfriend. Both Angie and her sister were thrown from the back of the station wagon. Angie suffered a broken jaw. Her sister suffered permanent brain damage.

At age five, Angie found her eleven-month-old sister dead in her crib from bronchial pneumonia. That same year, she watched in terror as her mother was brutally beaten by a boyfriend. Angie, too, suffered the same fate from time to time. She lived in fear of all men.

When she was six, her mother's newest boyfriend burned their home down. They lost everything except the clothes on their back. Angie's mother fled with her children from California to Kansas with hopes of starting life anew. But tragedy followed.

At age nine, Angie's beloved uncle Tony died by suicide, hanging himself in a state hospital.

"He could sing like an angel. My last memory of him was when he put me on his lap, grabbed his guitar, and sang 'You Are My Sunshine.' As we left, I remember looking through the car window and feeling so sad for leaving him there," she said.

At age twelve, while getting her hair cut on Father's Day, Angie's intoxicated mother admitted the abuser Angie believed was her real father, was not her father at all.

At age thirteen, her close friend died from a virus. And the only grandmother Angie knew died from stomach cancer.

By age fourteen, Angie had taken to drugs and alcohol to mask the feeling of abandonment and grief. And to connect with her mother.

"I would feel like it was my way of being with her and connecting. The very thing that took her from us brought us together," shared Angie.

That same year, Angie's mother called social services to come get Angie's younger twin brothers.

"She was on a payphone, distraught, sobbing, and asked them to come get my brothers. I remember my emotions like it was yesterday, they are burned into my soul. They were my brothers and I couldn't save them. Though they didn't die, I grieved them so much," she said.

The boys were eventually adopted out. As the oldest of the seven children, Angie was devastated.

Her teenage years were filled with misery.

"I lived in foster homes on and off until the age of 18, due to alcoholism and drug abuse. It destroyed our family," shared Angie. "I felt very abandoned, like no one wanted me."

By age twenty-one, Angie had three small children of her own and was newly married to a different man. One night after partying, her husband was driving too fast on the back roads when he crashed their car. Dazed but able to free herself from the mangled wreck, Angie searched frantically for her husband in the dark field. Unable to find him, she ran to the nearest home for help. The police were called, but not the ambulance. Despite her pleas, they refused to believe Angie's account that her husband was still out there, somewhere in the field. She was arrested and hauled off to jail for drunk driving. Her husband's body was found the next day and, a few hours later, a diagonal bruise across Angie's chest from the passenger side seatbelt proved her innocence. But it was too late to save her husband.

More grief followed, and it came in many forms. Loss by suicide. Loss by homicide. More drugs, alcohol, and misery. Raising her three children while grieving her newlywed husband, Angie's attempts at sobriety met in failure until 2003, when she found sobriety for six years. She and her mother then relapsed together. Angie's was short lived, her mother's was not.

"The five years up to my mother's relapse had been the best in her life. She had reunited with the twins, and she had her children and grandchildren in her life. Her dreams were coming true. And then we relapsed together. I got sober, but mom didn't know if she could do it. Finally, she reached a doctor who gave her a prescription to help with the withdrawal symptoms, but the insurance wouldn't cover it. The sad part is that if she needed a pain killer, they would have paid for it," she said.

Angie's mother died of a drug overdose a few days later.

Wrought with grief and guilt, Angie was overcome with anger. Anger at her mother's life cut short. Anger at the system for failing them. Anger at her mother for being an addict. And anger that her mother had to grieve for her baby in silence all those years.

To cope with her fresh loss and fill the void in her heart, Angie turned to social media in hopes of finding other grievers to connect to. And found thousands just like herself. That was the moment Angie Cartwright found her calling.

In 2011, Angie created a Facebook group for grievers called Grief the Unspoken. And the movement to bring grief out of the dark and into the light was born.

In the four years since, Angie Cartwright is now considered a voice for grievers around the world. Her original Facebook group, now known as GTU, has grown into 24 open and closed groups with a weekly reach of over 2.5 million. Thousands more are connected via Twitter, Google Plus, Pinterest, and YouTube.

In 2013, Angie founded National Grief Awareness Day, a nonprofit organization dedicated to a day of grief awareness. In 2014, she became a cohost of Grief Diaries Radio and coauthored My Grief Diary, a workbook for grievers. At the beginning of 2015, Angie harnessed the power of the newest social media tool Flipboard to launch Grief Magazine, and in April 2015 she took the stage as a keynote speaker at the first National Grief & Hope Convention in Indianapolis.

"My mother lived in grief all her life. But she couldn't talk about it, people didn't want to hear about it. I became determined to bring grief out of the dark so others won't suffer in silence the way my mother did. I became her voice," shared Angie.

The memories remain fresh and some days the tears still flow, but Angie Cartwright is determined to make a difference for generations to come.

"It's about raising awareness and education, so people don't have to grieve in silence. Silent grief kills, which adds more grief. I don't grieve just for the moment my loved one passed. I grieve the past, the future, and the now. A human being is more than just one moment in time," she stated. "And the time has come to bring grief out of the dark and into the light."

ABOUT

ANGIE CARTWRIGHT

Angie Cartwright is the founder of National Grief Awareness Day, occurring on August 30 of each year. She is also the co-founder of We Care Grief Support. Angie has experienced the pain of loss many times in her life starting with the loss of her baby sister when Angie was just 5 years old, the loss of Angie's newlywed husband from a tragic car accident at the tender age of 21, and the loss of her mother from an accidental overdose. Learning the hard way that grievers are often misunderstood, Angie is committed to help change how our culture understands and views grief. She expertly coaches and comforts people all around the world through social media, her website, and her Grief Release Course, to help them find solid footing once again. "I finally realized there was only one thing I could ever do to be free," shares Angie. "It was to embrace my humanness."

angie@nationalgriefawarenessday.org
www.nationalgriefawarenessday.com

ALYBLUE MEDIA TITLES

Grief Diaries: Victim Impact Statement

Grief Diaries: Hit by Impaired Driver

Grief Diaries: Surviving Loss of a Spouse

Grief Diaries: Surviving Loss of a Child

Grief Diaries: Surviving Loss of a Sibling

Grief Diaries: Surviving Loss of a Parent

Grief Diaries: Surviving Loss of an Infant

Grief Diaries: Surviving Loss of a Loved One

Grief Diaries: Surviving Loss by Suicide

Grief Diaries: Surviving Loss of Health

Grief Diaries: How to Help the Newly Bereaved

Grief Diaries: Loss by Impaired Driving

Grief Diaries: Loss by Homicide

Grief Diaries: Loss of a Pregnancy

Grief Diaries: Hello from Heaven

Grief Diaries: Grieving for the Living

Grief Diaries: Shattered

Grief Diaries: Project Cold Case

Grief Diaries: Poetry & Prose and More

Grief Diaries: Through the Eyes of Men

Grief Diaries: Will We Survive?

Real Life Diaries: Living with a Brain Injury

Real Life Diaries: Through the Eyes of DID

Real Life Diaries: Through the Eyes of an Eating Disorder

Real Life Diaries: Living with Endometriosis

Real Life Diaries: Living with Mental Illness

Grammy Visits From Heaven

Grandpa Visits From Heaven

Faith, Grief & Pass the Chocolate Pudding

Heaven Talks to Children

Color My Soul Whole

Grief Reiki

A Child is Missing: A True Story

A Child is Missing: Searching for Justice

walking with a friend in the dark
is better than walking alone in the light.
HELEN KELLER

*

PUBLISHED BY ALYBLUE MEDIA
Inside every human is a story worth sharing.
www.AlyBlueMedia.com

75795534R00063

Made in the USA
Columbia, SC
24 August 2017